P🐾SiTiVeLY GeORgia

The MOTiVaTiONaL TaLe Of a UNiQUe aiReDaLe

Elizabeth Ferris

Published by
Hasmark Publishing
www.hasmarkpublishing.com

Permission should be addressed in writing to Elizabeth Ferris at lizferris2017@gmail.com

Illustrations: Matrix Solutions

Editor: Corinne Casazza
corinnecasazza@gmail.com

Layout: Anne Karklins
anne@hasmarkpublishing.com

ISBN 13: 978-1-989756-11-9
ISBN 10: 1989756115

Norman, thank you for your endless love and support and giving me the best years of my life.

Hello, I shall start by introducing myself. My name is Georgia and I'm ten years young. My breed is an Airedale Terrier, and my family tree of Airedales is believed to have started out in the West Riding of Yorkshire, England. I currently live in Western Canada with my human, Norman.

I've been told that I'm 'big boned' as I'm twice the size I'm supposed to be. It's funny because I don't feel 'big boned'. I feel unique and special.

I am a pretty lucky Airedale. My Norman takes me on many adventures. He calls it "going to work," but for me I get to ride along in his big black truck and visit the people and places he gets to visit. I really like to bark at everyone that comes near his truck. It's fun for me to hear my own voice. I think I have a great voice, and by the length of this book you can tell I have lots to say.

I've heard that I'm a rescue dog. I don't remember much as I was only 3 years old when I moved to my new home, but I do know the minute I saw my Norman, I chose him and we are buddies for life.

I can tell my Norman really loves me. On warm, sunny days he takes me swimming in the river down by his work, and the rest of the time I get to travel on every appointment he goes to. He says I'm the company mascot. It's a pretty good job being the company mascot and I get treated really well.

My Norman only buys me the highest quality of dog food. He takes me to the doggy hair salon to get freshened up a couple times a year, and I am very lucky as I have four fluffy giant beds in various locations to keep me cozy, well rested, and content. One bed is in the living room, another in the back of his canopy covered truck, one in the bedroom, (I like to stare at him when he sleeps) and even one in the garage so we can always be together. I can tell he really, really unconditionally loves me as sometimes I have an accident and poop in his truck, but he cleans up my mess and doesn't get mad at me. He makes a joke sometimes so that I don't feel ashamed. He says, "Bad burritos Georgia?"

As I sleep, I like to daydream when I'm not barking at people or things. I shut down my sharp sense of smell and activate my creative imagination instead. I like to create and dream. I feel like I'm the star of my own movie and I can make anything happen because I'm directing it.

4

I imagine great things. I imagine that I am popular all over the world and people really love to hear my 'Georgia' thoughts as I strive to only speak positive, helpful words. I like to make people smile and laugh and feel good about themselves.

I feel like everyone should express who they truly are, and feel the amazing energy they have within them and know they can accomplish marvellous things if they just believe in themselves.

I believe in you. We all have so much to give and I hope when you daydream you feel a sense of pride in yourself for being you. You are the only you! What a gift! You are already ahead of me as you don't poop in the truck. Good job.

When I start my day, I feel excited and look forward to what the day may bring. I like to get the energy flowing by running up and down the hallway, smiling ear-to-ear as my paws and claws hit the wood floor with a "click, click, click, click," like I'm tap dancing to the world in excitement. I do believe that how you start your day determines how the rest of your day goes.

I used to start my day by going to the toilet bowl and taking a big, huge drink of water. Then I'd run around the house with water dripping everywhere until I found something to wipe my furry, wet face on. I loved wiping my face on pant legs and bed spreads. When we had company over to visit and I soaked them all with my toilet bowl dribbles, they would always ask "Why Georgia, Why?" Eventually I realized that if I want to up my game and be the best Airedale I can be, I better up the standard I had for myself. Did I want to be known as 'Georgia, the toilet bowl dog?' That didn't feel like the best use of my time here on Earth.

I will admit, it does take constant, daily focus and a decision for me to keep going in the right direction to be the best I can be. I have decided to resist the urge to go back to my old toilet bowl drinking habits.

After ten years of being me, I know that nothing happens until you make a decision. You have to want to change. To gain confidence, you have to take action. make a decision, and then do it. I feel much more confident now that I don't have toilet bowl breath.

One day I decided I would be the most positive, motivational Airedale ever! I help people by spreading positive messages to the world and continuously reminding people of their awesomeness. I do know that everyone of us has doubts about something, but you have to keep going and know everything will work out amazingly well once you make a decision to be better. We all have unique gifts to share with the world. Think, then decide, and then head in that direction. You must be able to think. If the thought of quitting enters your mind, focus.

Focus on your true potential and success, and it will be yours. You are here for a reason. Share your gifts.

I remember when I was little, I would lift my leg and pee a bit here and there and everywhere like I was marking a route back and I wasn't even lost. I'm a girl dog so my aim was a little off and I was forever having wet fur on my leg. I'm not sure why I did it. I think I just saw another dog do it, so I thought I was supposed to do it too. I would hear my Norman say, "Monkey see, monkey do." I was definitely in the habit of following the pack of monkeys.

These days I make sure to watch my habits and not be a pack animal. Are you ready to break free from the monkey business too? I think you should. Everyone wants to see what creative ideas you have to offer.

Another habit I had was to rip up two of my beds during the days my Norman didn't take me to work with him. I'd get so frustrated and the voice in my head would say things like "you are staying home because you don't deserve to go.'"

I usually ended the day with white fluff scattered from kitchen to the bedroom, not to mention a cotton ball taste in my mouth. Oh, so very, very dry. Not recommended. When my Norman came home, I'd hide my face in a corner of a room so he couldn't see me.

My Norman is so nice though. He would just go get me another bed, and another, and another. I'm pretty sure the store thinks he has about fifty dogs.

That little voice of mine sure cost my Norman a lot of money for cotton mouth. That voice in my head has gotten me into other types of trouble as well, but now I know to stop that voice. If I find myself starting to get anywhere near trouble, I tell myself... "Stop digging,

Georgia... Stop digging!"

Sometimes I hear people tell my Norman they can't believe I'm ten years old. I don't feel old. I think the secret to a long life is best summed up by remembering, once you get going, the energy will start flowing. For example, my Norman likes to bring me to the river to swim. At first, I was afraid to swim, plus I didn't want to get my ears wet, but he threw a stick into the water, and oh man, do I ever like a good stick!

I had to just make the leap and just go for it. I told myself my ears would dry. You are mine, stick! I hope you know that there is no end to what you are capable of doing either. Gather up your energy, make up your mind you'll be successful at whatever you do, and then just go do it. Fetch that stick! I'm very grateful the energy found me that day I decided to face my fear and jump in the river. The energy has stayed with me ever since.

I know I've mentioned this already, but it's worth repeating. My Norman is so kind. He stays near me while I swim in the river because he thinks I will float away. He doesn't realize what an exceptional swimmer I actually am, but that's okay. He thinks it's funny to pretend he is fishing with me. He pretends he is holding a fishing pole and says "caught me a Marlin!" His fish jokes are silly and I'm glad. He likes to use his imagination in a positive way just like me.

20

I realize that not all people are positive like me and my Norman. One day the neighbour Jake came up to me while I was walking around the block. Jake uses his imagination in a negative way. He is a small 'ankle biter' type dog. He always sounds like he's barking really fast and his voice is so high. He constantly barks like something is on fire! I listened to his stories that day and realized something about him. He spoke badly about everyone, even Roger the horse who lives in a field in the country by Norman's and my house. Roger is a very nice horse who wouldn't speak badly about anybody. How could Jake say such things that weren't true?

Jake had nothing good to say at all about any-body or anything. He was all negative bark and I felt my insides get all worked up just listening to him. My emotions were changing and I felt like I needed to eat a bunch of grass to settle my stomach, or I would throw up all over this 'ankle biter' of a creature.

At that moment I realized that if I hang out with the wrong types of animals, I won't be heading in the direction I want to go. I told Jake I had to head home as my Norman was waiting for me. I left, and I never looked back.

The next time I saw Roger the horse, I made sure to tell him how much I appreciated how he was always kind to everyone. I even brought him a carrot from the garden and he slobbered all over my face while he ate.

I know that some days it's hard to remain positive and upbeat. We do pick up what others are feeling sometimes. If I start to feel sad, or angry, or any other emotion besides happy, I trick my brain and pretend I'm happy even when I feel blue, as I realize now that the world is what you make it.

I think it's far better to spend my days as a positive, happy Airedale rather than being upset. When it comes to people, my Norman says "you only need to have four quarters around you, rather than 100 pennies." I SO agree, as I do believe we start to behave like the creatures we interact with most.

I think it's best to only accept advice from those that have proven results of what you want to accomplish. The 'ankle biter' lifestyle is definitely not for me. I would hang out with Roger the slobber horse anytime.

Speaking of hanging out, my Norman and I live in the country and I have the neighbourhood mapped out by smell. There is another creature I try to avoid as I find her hard to understand. Sasha-Patrice, the neighbourhood big, fluffy black cat. I try to stay away from Sasha-Patrice because I can feel her sending out negative energy.

The other day, Sasha-Patrice snuck up on me when I was daydreaming in the sunshine in the front yard. She is always talking about the weather. She says things like "smells like rain," "there is a big storm brewing," "some big, scary thunderstorms are on their way." I'm not sure why she is always willing the storms to come. It was a bright, sunny, glorious, amazing day. She dislikes heavy rain, yet she talks about it all the time.

I like to look at things differently. I like to talk about the things I want and love. I really enjoy the sunshine, and I am grateful for the here and now, and for my Norman and all our adventures together. Rather than talking about bad things that may or may not occur, I like to focus on being happy and present in the moment.

The moment we are in now is the most important moment, I believe, as once it passes it is gone forever. I don't want to miss anything in the movie of my life.

My goal in life is to bring joy to all humans. When I started to do good things for myself and help others, I truly started to like myself more. I am a proud Airedale now. I feel like when I put good out, it always comes back to me in the most unexpected ways.

The other day while at work with my Norman, we stopped to look at a house for sale in the big city. That is what my Norman does. He helps people get new homes and sell their old ones. He has been doing this for over twenty-five years and is really good at it. I'm happy and proud to be his official mascot.

At the house, there was a little girl sitting on the porch step who looked a little blue. I had the feeling she was sad she would have to leave her house and move away soon. I went up to her and gave her the biggest, sloppiest, wettest kiss I could muster up from deep inside my furry soul. I then started to cuddle her by rubbing my 'big boned' furry body all over her tiny 'shorter than me' frame. The girl then began to smile and giggle a lot and hugged me back. She told me I was a good puppy. She told me stories about getting a puppy at her new house and going on many adventures together. She got so happy daydreaming out loud that she began to skip around the yard.

This is when I realized, when you send out good energy into the world, good energy comes back to you.

Once we got home from our 'house for sale' adventures, my Norman walked into the kitchen and I followed him. He asked me if I wanted a treat. He said, "Bacon, the maple kind?"

My brain right away said "Bacon?... I never get Bacon!" I was like "Yes Please! Yes Please!" I jumped up and down, smiling ear-to-ear as my paws and claws went "click, click, click, click" on the kitchen floor. I could tap dance to the world in excitement every day over bacon!

I realized again, when you send out good energy into the world, good energy comes back to you in the most unexpected ways, just like 'bacon' snacks!

For me, the secret to having that good energy with me all the time is to hold a positive picture in mind. The picture in my mind now is of my Norman and our next happy adventures together and how I can help spread helpful energy all over the world just by being me, Positively Georgia.

I think in your mind, you have to come up with something you really want and then work backwards. For example, in my mind I'm now holding a picture of travelling on a big cruise ship with my Norman as I love water so much. I'm learning how to focus in on that and feel what it feels like and trust and expect for that to show up in my life. That pesky voice started to tell me "dogs can't go on cruise ships!" I think it's natural sometimes to doubt in one's abilities. You hear that pesky inside voice that tries to destroy dreams and wants to bring you down.

It has taken me ten years but I'm getting really good at telling that pesky unhelpful voice to stop. I realize now yes dogs can, if they are service dogs! I'm going to start taking service dog training and provide comfort and emotional support to all that need me. From my rescue dog beginnings to finding my true potential as a service dog, I'm moving forward with my exciting life, full steam ahead.

If you have doubts sometimes like I did, I hope my words will help give you direction and calm your mind and that you now begin to feel happy and grateful for each day. We have each been given a joyous gift – the gift of realizing our true potential.

These days I'm feeling pretty self-confident and I'm ready for great undertakings. I'm definitely not 'Georgia, the toilet bowl' dog anymore. I have totally upped my personal standard and hold myself accountable and responsible for my happiness. I wrote this book and I can't even speak human or type. I just had to get on the right 'bark' frequency and all my daydreams are coming true. My hope for you is that you decide what you truly want and then go do it. Time moves quickly and waits for no one. The quicker you start making your dreams happen the better. You have vast potential! Let it happen. Share your gifts with the world like me. Smile ear-to-ear and get your paws and claws going "click, click, click, click" and tap dance to the world in excitement too.

The eND.

36

HEARTS to be HEARD

Giving a Voice to Creativity!

Your donation will give a voice to the creativity
that lies within the hearts of physically,
spiritually and mentally challenged children.

By helping us publish their books,
musical creations and works of art you will
make a difference in a child's life;
a child who would not otherwise be heard.

Donate now by going to
HeartstobeHeard.com

The children thank you!!

About the Author

Georgia Ferris lives with her humans Elizabeth and Norman in Northern British Columbia, Canada. Georgia is working on her next book about travelling outside Canada, spreading her 'Georgia' thoughts of positivity one country at a time. She doesn't poop in the truck anymore.

www.ferrisbooks.com

Made in the USA
Monee, IL
10 March 2020

22973345R00026